SNOOPY

features as

The Fitness Fanatic

D0774330

ЯR

500 587585

Printed and bound in Great Britain
for Ravette Publishing Limited,
Unit 3, Tristar Centre,
Star Road, Partridge Green,
West Sussex RH13 8RA
by Cox & Wyman, Berkshire.

ISBN: 1 84161 029 1

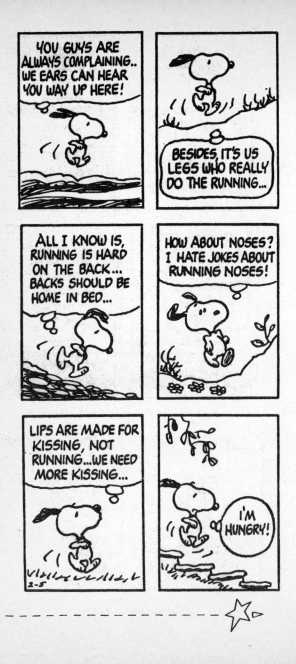

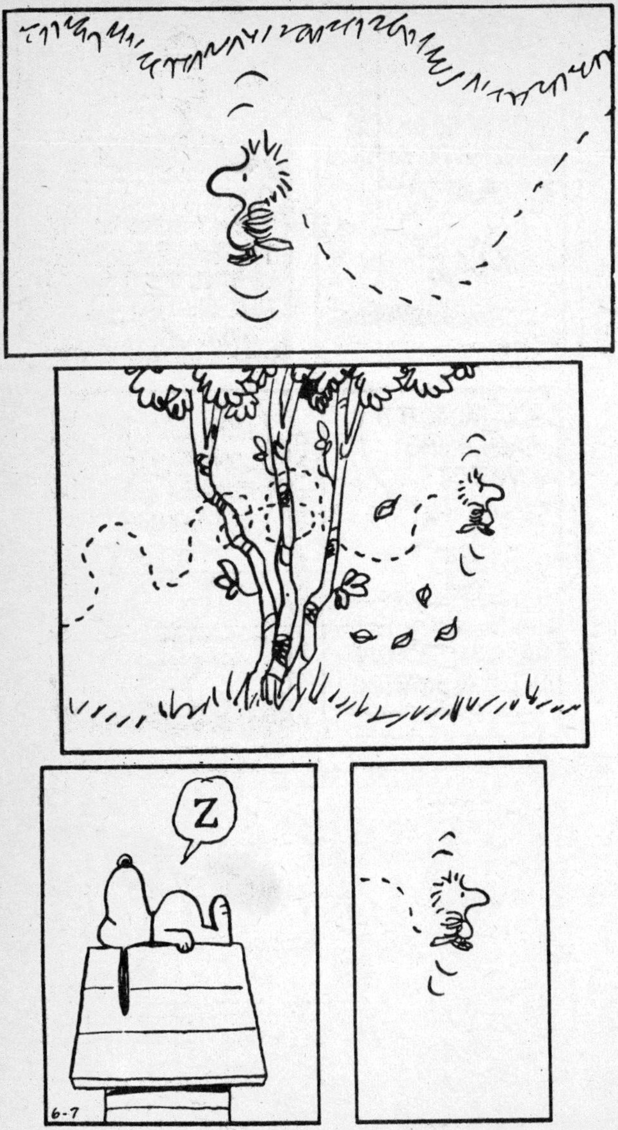
Z
6-7

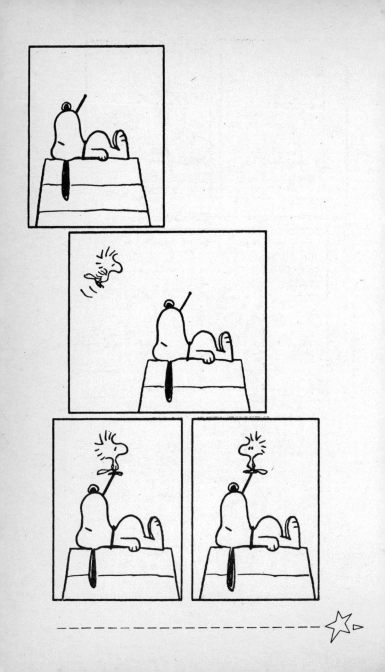

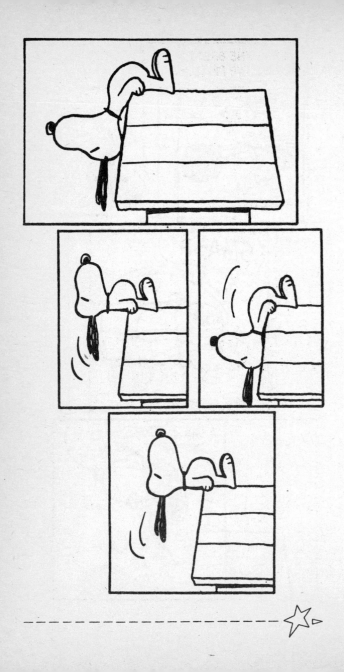

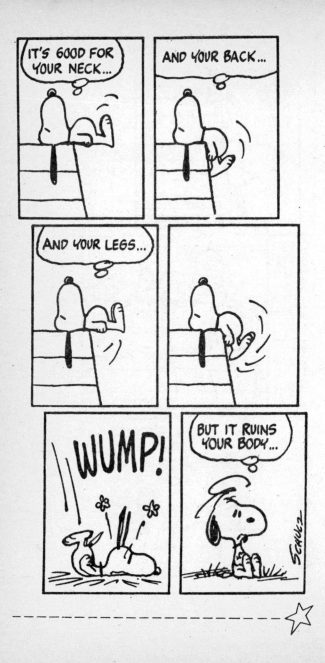

Other PEANUTS™ titles published by Ravette ...

Snoopy Features as ...

The Literary Ace	1 84161 026 7	£2.99
The Flying Ace	1 84161 027 5	£2.99
The Matchmaker	1 84161 028 3	£2.99

Snoopy Laughter and Learning series
wipe clean pages
(a fun series of story and activity books for preschool
and infant school children)

available July 2000

Read with Snoopy	1 84161 016 X	£2.50
Write with Snoopy	1 84161 017 8	£2.50
Count with Snoopy	1 84161 018 6	£2.50
Colour with Snoopy	1 84161 019 4	£2.50

PEANUTS™ Anniversary Treasury
(224 pages featuring some of Charlie Brown's favourite
strips in colour and black & white)

available August 2000	1 84161 021 6	£9.99

You Really Don't Look 50, Charlie Brown
(over 500 daily and Sunday strips and a series of
Charles Schulz essays celebrating this anniversary
year).

available Sept 2000	1 84161 020 8	£6.99

All PEANUTS™ books are available from your local bookshop or from the address below. Just tick the titles required and send the form with your payment to:-

BBCS, P.O. Box 941, Kingston upon Hull HU1 3YQ
24-hr telephone credit card line 01482 224626

Prices and availability are subject to change without prior notice.

Please enclose a cheque or postal order made payable to BBCS to the value of the cover price of the book and allow the following for postage and packing:-

UK & BFPO:	£1.95 (weight up to 1kg)	3-day delivery
	£2.95 (weight over 1kg up to 20kg)	3-day delivery
	£4.95 (weight up to 20kg)	next day delivery
EU & Eire:	Surface Mail: £2.50 for first book & £1.50 for subsequent books	
	Airmail: £4.00 for first book & £2.50 for subsequent books	
USA:	Surface Mail: £4.50 for first book & £2.50 for subsequent books	
	Airmail: £7.50 for first book & £3.50 for subsequent books	
Rest of the World:	Surface Mail: £6.00 for first book & £3.50 for subsequent books	
	Airmail: £10.00 for first book & £4.50 for subsequent books	

Name: ....

Address: ....

....

....

Cards accepted: Visa, Mastercard, Switch, Delta, American Express

Expiry date .... Signature ....